On the Edge
The First 200 Days

By
Joe Martin
and
Dr. Jon Carlson

FOREWORD....

On The Edge touches the soul! This book contains the first 200 cartoons and is full of laughs coupled with sound psychological advice. It is possible to laugh yourself to a more satisfying life. Joe Martin is America's premier cartoonist (his cartoons even appear in *Chicken Soup for the Soul*) and Jon Carlson is a "Legend" in the counseling profession. This interesting combination provides a creative and effective way to deal with life's many challenges.

Read the book slowly, maybe take a cartoon a day, and see how the "gripes" can be faced with a smile and some action. The "gripes" are universal, the normal kinds of problems that we all face. Soon you will find that you are smiling your way through challenges that previously left you frustrated. You will realize that you are not alone in your troubles. Read these cartoons and get "off the edge" and back onto solid ground.

Jack Canfield
Co-Creator of *The Chicken Soup for the Soul* series

PREFACE....

As a Professor and practicing psychologist, my research puts me in regular contact with the leaders in the field. In sharing *On the Edge* with them, I found universal support for the powerful healing potential of this concept.

I first used Joe Martin's cartoons when I edited *The Family Journal*. They not only related well to the articles, but made learning a fun activity. Over the years, having the cartoons on hand, I found myself using them to connect with my patients when words failed. The humor, relating to their specific problem, brought the walls down. After the laughter they realized that they were not alone with their troubles. They could look at their problem with a totally new and healthy perspective. We had connected deeply and the most difficult part of my job was over !!

On the Edge probably began the day I ran into Joe Martin at Starbuck's after working with a particularly troubled patient. I explained how the man was *on the edge* of a nervous breakdown after a series of major disasters. He was in a frenzied state when I showed him one of the *Mr. Boffo* cartoons. Joe's initial response was a shocked, "You did what?". He wasn't aware of the success I'd been having with this technique over the years and thought I'd come to tell him about a pending lawsuit. I immediately explained the calming effect of the joke. The first panel of the joke showed two men falling down a bottomless pit frantically screaming and the second panel showed the same two men six months later, relaxed and totally bored. It was easy to see how the patient connected with this and saw how his frenzy was only temporary.

At this point Joe surprised me with the idea of this being a much-needed feature in the newspapers. This started our four-year development program with the cooperation of several local newspapers and many of my colleagues. You can see the end result on the following pages. All of the *On the Edge* panels have appeared in newspapers around the country from the *San Diego Union-Tribune* and the *Orange County Register* to the *Fort Lauderdale Sun-Sentinel*.

I hope you enjoy *On the Edge* and see how many of the gripes you can identify with.

Dr. Jon Carlson

ON THE EDGE with Earl, Nadine & Weederman

BY JOE MARTIN & DR. JON CARLSON

SHRINK WRAPPED

"WHY CAN'T SOMEONE HELP ME?"

You need to help yourself. **Fact: Researchers have long known that mental health improves dramatically when you get along with the significant people in your life.** Try to improve these relationships one at a time.

ON THE EDGE with Earl, Nadine & Weederman

BY JOE MARTIN & DR. JON CARLSON

ONE MORE TIME AROUND PLEASE, PLEASE, PLEASE, PLEASE!

A BIG PART OF THE REASON ASTRONAUTS DON'T LIKE TO TAKE THEIR KIDS ON SPACE SHUTTLE MISSIONS

"WE NEVER HAVE FUN ANYMORE."

"Fun" is the other three-letter word adults don't get enough of. Children laugh about 300 times a day, while an adult laughs 17 times per day. Observe a child today and learn to find delight in ordinary things.

'WHY AM I STUCK WITH THIS MOPE?"

You will probably be "stuck" with any partner you choose. Research shows that three out of four people who get divorced are still unhappy. You need to learn how to change and be a different partner, rather then finding a new one. Think of a time you and your partner were happy. Can you act that same way today?

"TIME SEEMS TO HEAL EVERYONE ELSE'S WOUNDS, WHY DOESN'T IT WORK FOR ME?"

In addition to time, some treatment or action can help. It is a medical fact that loving others eases pain. Try to show love to one other person today.

'WHY DO I HAVE TO GET OLD?'

The only way to escape aging is to die young.
Research shows that your age has more to do
with your attitude than with years lived. You can
be old or young at any age. Try acting younger in
one way today. (Hula-Hoop? Yo-Yo?)

"WHY DOES HE DRINK SO MUCH WHEN WE GO OUT?"

Many people drink as a way of self-medicating for social anxi-
ety which takes many forms: boredom, insecurity, or out-and-
out panic. Some experts estimate that 25% of the population
suffers with this problem. If your partner is one of the 25%,
try to make an effort to help them connect with you and the
other people you are with - without the alcohol buffer.

THERE'S TWENTY-FOUR HOURS IN A DAY AND TWENTY-FOUR BEERS IN A CASE AND SHE THINKS IT'S JUST COINCIDENCE

"MY HUSBAND USES CONVOLUTED LOGIC TO JUSTIFY ANYTHING HE DOES."

As you know, arguing with him doesn't work, so do something different and start agreeing with him. "Give him enough rope and he'll hang himself." Fasten your seatbelt as life will be very interesting for a few weeks.

ON THE EDGE with Earl, Nadine & Weederman

BY JOE MARTIN & DR. JON CARLSON

FIRST WOMAN TO SCALE MT. EVEREST WITHOUT A BABY-SITTER

"WE BOTH WORK, SO WHY AM I ALWAYS THE DESIGNATED BABY-SITTER?"

Since the 70's, the number of women in the work-force has risen dramatically, but the attitudes haven't kept pace. Talk to your partner about up-dating your roles, and learn to share both work and home responsibilities.

ON THE EDGE
with Earl, Nadine & Weederman

BY JOE MARTIN & DR. JON CARLSON

"WHY DO I ALWAYS GO CRAZY OVER THE SLIGHTEST LITTLE THING, WHILE OTHERS, WAY WORSE THAN ME, NEVER SEEM BOTHERED AT ALL?"

It is a known fact that our response to stress is learned. Over time it becomes a pattern. Some people learn to fly kites when they are challenged, while others go "crazy". Try a new response and begin to break the pattern.

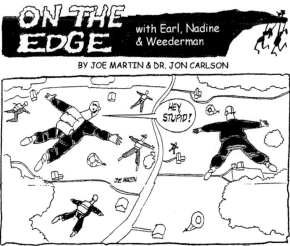

ON THE EDGE
with Earl, Nadine & Weederman

BY JOE MARTIN & DR. JON CARLSON

"NEXT TIME MY BOSS CALLS ME A NAME IN FRONT OF EVERYONE, I'M DECKING HIM."

Names often stick to people, and the silliest ones are the most adhesive. Only accept the ones that fit you. Remember, if the shoe fits, they'll kick you with it.

"WHY IS IT, NO MATTER HOW HARD I TRY, SOMETHING ALWAYS SEEMS TO GO WRONG?"

Fact: Successful people make just as many mistakes as others - the difference is they don't make the same one over and over. Next time something's about to fall on you, move out of the way.

"I'M NEVER TALKING TO MY SCREWY SISTER AGAIN...AND THIS TIME, I MEAN IT."

You learned how to handle family problems from your parents. They learned from theirs. If you check your family history, you'll probably find a long line of, let's call them, "time-outs". Change the pattern. Make a peace offering, and end the thousand-years' war.

"I SLEPT UNTIL NOON AGAIN TODAY."

FACT: You're a self-made man. You owe your lack of success to nobody. Everybody wants to be good at something, you have become the best at doing nothing. Be careful, as ambition can get you into a lot of hard work.

"I'M GOING OUT OF MY MIND! WHY AM I SO BORED?"

According to psychologist, Erich Fromm, "Only humans can be bored." A roller coaster can be boring, but not the first time. Once a week plan to do something you've never done before. Anticipation is half the fun.

DO I REALLY NEED ALL THESE PILLS?

There's a good chance you don't. Many believe if one pill is good, two must be twice as good! 15 million (and growing) are addicted to prescription drugs! Check with your physician, and another one, about what you are taking.

"WHY DO I ALWAYS MAKE THE WRONG DECISIONS WHEN IT COMES TO MONEY?"

FACT: The better we think something will make us feel (like money), the more we want it. The truth is that even in great quantities money doesn't bring happiness. A year or two after winning the lottery, the winners were no happier than before striking it rich! Focus on making decisions that create happiness, and see if your bad luck continues.

"THE IRS AUDIT IS RUINING MY LIFE, I CAN'T THINK OF ANYTHING ELSE."

Crazy is as crazy does. Audits don't drive us crazy, it's the way we approach the audit. Expect trouble, and that's what you'll get. View the auditor as your friend, bring him coffee and a bagel. And maybe there's some truth to the legend about the man who was audited and ended up getting a refund.

"I'VE HAD IT UP TO HERE WITH MISTER-KNOW-IT-ALL."

Oscar Wilde said, "I am not young enough to know everything." Here's your situation. Some people believe that the more they know, the more people will like them. Knowing this, may in some way help ease your pain.

BY JOE MARTIN & DR. JON CARLSON

"WHY IS IT ALWAYS MY FAULT?"

MAYBE IT IS YOU!? If it walks like a duck, sounds like a duck and looks like a duck, maybe you're a duck! Contrary to popular opinion, it is possible to be wrong all the time. Most people have learned to "duck" responsibility by blaming someone or something for problems that can only be fixed by them. Try taking the blame one time, and see what happens.

BY JOE MARTIN & DR. JON CARLSON

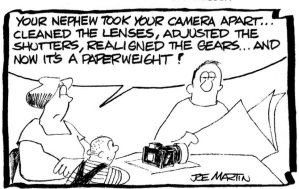

"WHY CAN'T PEOPLE LEAVE MY STUFF ALONE?"

Families have developed an overly casual attitude about personal property. The line between sharing and taking has become clouded. Before you start tagging everything, try making and keeping these boundaries clear.

BY JOE MARTIN & DR. JON CARLSON

"DO I HAVE TO PUT UP WITH MY HUSBAND'S WISECRACKS ABOUT MY FAMILY AND FRIENDS?"

This may be one of those 10 to 12 annoying things our partner does that will never change. Back off-- remember the Buddhist Law of Karma (loosely translated): What Goes Around, Comes Around.

"WHY AM I ALWAYS PUTTING MY FOOT IN MY MOUTH? I CRINGE WHEN I THINK OF SOME OF THE DUMB THINGS I SAY."

You're probably from the "saying-anything-is-better-than-nothing" school. The truth is everyone is a fool for 5 to 10 minutes a day. Next time there's a lull in the conversation, and you get that familiar urge - Put a sock in it.

"WE DON'T HAVE ANY MONEY!"

What do you have? Focus on that, and if all you have are problems, at least you have things to keep you busy.

"EVERYONE IS RIPPING ME OFF! WHEN IS IT MY TURN?"

Don't be in a hurry to take your turn in the Dunk Tank. The lowest common denominator is not the way to go.

"WHY DO I HAVE TO LEARN EVERY-THING THE HARD WAY?"

We all have different learning styles. At least you're learning, and that's 90% of the battle.

WHY ARE MY CHILDREN SO UNGRATEFUL?

Research shows that our children are growing up too quickly and facing the pressures of adulthood too early. What is good for adults is not good for children! Kids are stressed, depressed, and lack interest in activities. Try treating your children like children, and see if more gratitude comes your way.

"WHY DO I ATTRACT ALL THE WEIRDOS?"

FACT: You can be accessible and inviting to a fault--it's the dark side of charisma. Try not making eye contact with anyone with tattoo sleeves, for starters.

"WHY CAN'T I FIND RESPONSIBLE HELP?"

You need to be responsible first. Don't wish yourself into trouble by convincing yourself that someone is capable when deep-down you know they're not. Sam Goldwyn once said, "Next time I want a fool to do something, I'll send myself."

"HOW COULD I BE SO STUPID?"

Don't focus on the negative! "Everyone is ignorant, only on different subjects." (Will Rogers) We are all smart and dumb in some areas. What areas are you proficient in? Learn to play down your liabilities and praise your strengths.

"DOESN'T ANYBODY LISTEN TO ANYTHING I SAY?"

Tuning out spouses has become the national habit. Some experts have figured that miscommunications occur as high as 90 percent of the time. Try listening to every word the next time your partner says something.

BY JOE MARTIN & DR. JON CARLSON

MAN WHO LOST HIS JOB, HIS WIFE AND HIS FAVORITE TIE-PIN ON THE SAME DAY

"MY HUSBAND DOESN'T KNOW I EXIST."

The leading complaint that marriage counselors receive is "I don't feel important anymore." You need to get off the bench, back into the game, or traded to another team.

ON THE EDGE with Earl, Nadine & Weederman

BY JOE MARTIN & DR. JON CARLSON

"THERE YOU ARE!! I THOUGHT YOU WERE HOME! YA KNOW, .." WE ALMOST LEFT WHEN YOU DIDN'T ANSWER THE DOOR!

"WHY CAN'T WE MAKE ANY FRIENDS?"

FACT: Social isolation is on the rise. Not everybody wants a friend - those that do are active and outgoing. You'll find them in church groups, doing volunteer work, or taking classes. Start looking. It's time to widen your horizons.

"IS IT NORMAL FOR SOMEONE TO LIE ABOUT EVERYTHING ALL THE TIME?"

People often lie and exaggerate when they are caught at something. System theory states that if one person changes, the other will as well. Meditate and contemplate on the mysteries in YOUR own life, instead of "policing" your partner.

"MY HUSBAND DRIVES LIKE A MANIAC."

FACT: Over 80% of us are involved in road rage. Beware of the urge of courage, it leads to nothing but trouble. Try to get out of the fast lane, even if it's just a little bit each day.

"I'M SUPPOSED TO PROTECT THE HOUSE, BUT THEY'VE GOT MY HANDS TIED."

People want their dogs to do it all. Even dogs can't be everything to everybody. Do you want a lover, a fighter, or something in between? Vets tell me Chihuahuas bark the most.

"I HAVEN'T GOT TIME TO VACUUM TEN TIMES A DAY, HOW DO I GET MY MOTHER OFF MY BACK?"

LEGAL FACT: Mothers can only ruin the first 18 years of your life, the remainder is up to you. Next time your mother comes to roam, tell her to wear her toga.

ON THE EDGE with Earl, Nadine & Weederman

BY JOE MARTIN & DR. JON CARLSON

"LIFT THAT GATE, BOY, IT'S TOLL GATE TOMMY -- HE RIDES FREE!"

"I'M AFRAID TO GET IN THE CAR WITH MY HUSBAND. HE DRIVES LIKE A MANIAC."

Fact: Fear either motivates or paralyzes. Many people are paralyzed and just give into others as if they have no other choices. Find motivation from your fear and tell your husband to grow up or you're taking a cab. Make it a limo.

ON THE EDGE with Earl, Nadine & Weederman

BY JOE MARTIN & DR. JON CARLSON

EL SICKO ALL TIME GROSS - OUT CARDS

"OH, HON.. HERE'S A CUTE ONE"

"WHY ARE MEN SO GROSS?"

Fact: Men are more attracted to visual stimuli. Scientists believe it is hard-wired in the genes. You don't have to like it, but you probably need to accept it - the silk purse/sow's ear thing.

ON THE EDGE

with Earl, Nadine & Weederman

BY JOE MARTIN & DR. JON CARLSON

"Ya know, this proves how goofy you are!...You could've gotten me the beer, found the TV page and changed the channel in one-tenth the time it took to pack all my things."

"HE NEVER TAKES ME SERIOUS, BUT ONE OF THESE DAYS I REALLY WILL LEAVE."

Remember the Chinese proverb: Talk does not cook rice. He doesn't take you serious because you are not serious. Try doing something different, like talking to another man and see if he notices you.

ON THE EDGE

with Earl, Nadine & Weederman

BY JOE MARTIN & DR. JON CARLSON

"DON'T HIT THAT SNACK TRAY TOO HEAVY...I WAS JUST KIDDING WHEN I SAID WE WERE INVITED"

"I CAN'T REMEMBER THE LAST TIME MY HUSBAND TOOK ME ANYWHERE NICE".

FACT: No one can read your mind! Maybe he doesn't know what you mean by "nice"? He may believe that you and he really like the same things - after all, you're married! Let him know that you would like to dine out somewhere other than a drive-through place.

"I CAN'T TELL YOU ENOUGH WHAT A KICK MY BRIDGE CLUB GETS OUT OF YOU TWO"

"I TRUSTED MY BEST FRIEND WITH A VERY PERSONAL SECRET AND NOW I FIND OUT SHE'S BLABBED IT ALL OVER TOWN."

FACT: Two can keep a secret if one of them is dead. It is not necessary to share EVERYTHING with friends - even good ones. Practice some restraint in what you do and whom you tell - in the meantime, lay low.

"ALL RIGHT, I'LL APOLOGIZE TO YOUR SISTER AND TO SHOW YOU HOW SINCERE I AM I'LL DO IT IN THE VOICE OF DONALD DUCK, HER FAVORITE CARTOON CHARACTER"

"EVERYTHING IS A JOKE TO HIM."

FACT: Too much of a good think is often a bad thing. Learn to develop balance by controlling your humorous side. Maybe just be funny on Tuesday?

ON THE EDGE with Earl, Nadine & Weederman

BY JOE MARTIN & DR. JON CARLSON

"AND IF IT'S TOO DEEP, YOU SIMPLY PUSH DOWN ON THE WATER-LEVEL CONTROL VALVE CONVENIENTLY ATTACHED TO YOUR ANKLE"

"WHY CAN'T WE EVER HAVE ANYTHING NICE?"

Fact: Most people live life as they were taught in their families of origin. The patterns are passed from one generation to the next. We tend to accept those life styles as normal. Let your partner know that this is no longer the case - *next time you're near Tiffany's.*

ON THE EDGE with Earl, Nadine & Weederman

BY JOE MARTIN & DR. JON CARLSON

"CAPITALIZE 'CREDIT MANAGER', PUT A COMMA BETWEEN 'ADDITIONAL LIABILITIES' AND 'FINANCIAL PRESSURE', A PERIOD AFTER 'REALIGN INSTALL-MENT SCHEDULE' AND HYPHENATE 'PIG-FACE'."

"WHAT AM I GOING TO DO ABOUT ALL THESE BILLS? I'M DROWNING IN DEBT."

FACT: According to George Prentice, "Some people use one half their ingenuity getting into debt, and the other half to avoid paying it." What else, besides avoiding and blaming, could you do to face your money problems? The bottom line is - more work, less stuff.

"LET'S SAVE SOME FOR TOMORROW...IF THERE'S ONE THING I LIKE BETTER THAN PIZZA, IT'S BREAKFAST IN BED."

"HE WON'T STOP EATING!"

Food addiction is a serious problem that affects 100% of the world's population. We think that only drugs and alchohol are a concern for abuse. Just because the government allows us to eat or drink things like coffee until the cows come home doesn't mean that it is not dangerous. Wake up or blow up!

CUSTOMER SERVICE

JOE MARTIN

" I GOT THE REFUND BUT DON'T DAWDLE.. I TOLD 'EM YOU HAD A GUN "

"EVEN IF HE DOES THE JOB, THERE WILL BE SOMETHING DONE WRONG."

Making mistakes can be a personality style. Eventually you give up your expectations for him and do it yourself. Sound familiar? Breathe deeply, and let him start and finish things, and learn about consequences.

"HE USED TO THINK THE WHOLE WORLD WAS AGAINST HIM, BUT NOW HE'S NARROWED IT DOWN TO ONE GUY WITH A HOSE"

"COULD THE FATES BE AGAINST ME? NOTHING EVER GOES MY WAY, I NEVER CATCH A BREAK"

FACT: The truth is the harder you work the more luck you'll find. As President James Garfield said, "A pound of pluck is worth a ton of luck." The problem is not so much that you do not get a break but the way you react. Many successful people go through long periods of bad luck.

ON THE EDGE
with Earl, Nadine & Weederman

BY JOE MARTIN & DR. JON CARLSON

"THE GUY THEY HIRED TO REPLACE ME STILL HASN'T SHOWN UP AND ALREADY THEY'VE NOTICED A MARKED IMPROVEMENT"

"WHENEVER HE IS GONE, EVERYTHING SEEMS BETTER."

Sometimes absence makes the heart grow fonder and sometimes it makes it wander. Researchers often take something away to see what effect it has. Even though we might work hard, we might not be working at the right things. Smile and agree with others, and see if you're more welcome at home.

ON THE EDGE
with Earl, Nadine & Weederman

BY JOE MARTIN & DR. JON CARLSON

"SHE'LL BE BACK... SHE'D NEVER LEAVE WITHOUT HER FAVORITE RAG"

"NO MATTER WHAT I DO OR SAY, HE DOESN'T GET IT!"

FACT: You can lead a horse to water but you can't make him drink. It is time to accept reality and stop banging your head against the wall. It's not going to happen. He is not going to change. Try putting this joke on the refrigerator.

ON THE EDGE
with Earl, Nadine & Weederman

BY JOE MARTIN & DR. JON CARLSON

OUR MARRIAGE COUNSELOR SAYS I MIGHT QUALIFY FOR AN UPGRADE!

"I THINK I CAN DO BETTER, SHOULD I SETTLE FOR SECOND BEST?"

The real question is, can YOU be a different partner? Most of the time we believe that we're wonderful and all we need to do is find a better partner. The truth is we need to BE a better partner. So what I would suggest is that you do all of the things you would do with "Mr. Wonderful" with "Mr. Mediocre", and see if it makes a difference.

"WHY CAN'T WE MEET NORMAL COUPLES?"

Normal couples want to be around other normal couples. Look in the mirror and see the problem! FACT: If you don't change direction, you'll end up where you're headed. Start doing three new activities each month, and get ready to meet your new best friends.

MY WIFE HAS NO INTEREST IN MY LIFE.

FACT: Men need to feel appreciated. When men feel value, they want to achieve. Perhaps your wife might be willing to show appreciation for your efforts, if not your actions? Let her know that you are at least trying. Remember what Herm Albright said, "A positive attitude may not solve all your problems, but it will annoy enough people to make it worth the effort."

ON THE EDGE

with Earl, Nadine & Weederman

BY JOE MARTIN & DR. JON CARLSON

"EVEN THE KIDS KNOW HE'S A FOOL, HOW CAN I GET HIM TO SHUT UP?"

You probably can't get him to be quiet, however, you can look at him in a different manner. As Mark Twain said, "Let us be thankful for fools. But for them, the rest of us could not succeed." You'll never look bad, as long as he is by your side!

ON THE EDGE

with Earl, Nadine & Weederman

BY JOE MARTIN & DR. JON CARLSON

"WE DON'T HAVE ANY GOALS."

You sound like Lily Tomlin, "I've always wanted to be somebody, but I see now I should have been more specific." People with goals are ten times more likely to reach them. Set one goal for this day, one for this week and another for the year. And put this on your refrigerator as a reminder.

"MY HUSBAND MIGHT AS WELL BE MARRIED TO THE TV.

FACT: 110% of Americans watch television daily. TV has replaced marriage in many homes!! Perhaps you can consider MEDIA FASTING and introduce yourself to the others who live in your house?

"HOW CAN I CONVINCE MY HUSBAND HIS IDEA IS CRAZY?"

Sometimes the best way to convince him he is wrong is to let him have his way. As the English proverb states, "Stupidity won't kill you, but it can make you sweat." Get out the fans as he learns a lesson.

"EVEN WHEN SHE TRIES, SHE CAN'T BE NICE TO ME."

Many people only feel comfortable when they are hurting others. We often take these hurts and insults from relatives, but seldom friends. Remind her of the Latin proverb, "If you speak insults, you will also hear them."

"WHY AM I HIS OWN PERSONAL SLAVE?"

Janis Joplin said, "Don't compromise yourself. You are all you got." Do whatever YOU believe makes you a good partner. Tell him to put his unfulfilled desires on his wish list in case the genie pops out of his empty beer bottle.

ON THE EDGE

with Earl, Nadine & Weederman

BY JOE MARTIN & DR. JON CARLSON

"IT CAN'T BE COINCIDENCE. EVERY TIME A JOB NEEDS TO BE DONE, HE HAS TO WORK ON HIS GREAT AMERICAN NOVEL."

According to Woody Allen, 80% of success is showing up. Pretending to write to get out of something is how to be a serious disappointment to yourself and others. Face what you are avoiding and get grounded in reality. Set deadlines. Either finish the novel, or finish painting the living room.

ON THE EDGE

with Earl, Nadine & Weederman

BY JOE MARTIN & DR. JON CARLSON

"MY HUSBAND'S OBSESSED ABOUT GOING BALD. WHAT'S THE BIG DEAL?"

"I want it long, straight, curly, fuzzy, shaggy, ratty, matty, oily, greasy, spangled and spaghettied." Theme from "Hair". FACT: By 35, one-third of all men experience some degree of baldness. Urge your husband to join a hair-loss support group where "we don't have room for drugs, plugs, or rugs, and we're proud of every hair we don't have."

THE WORLD AND THE WAY IT WOULD BE IF MY TWO SCREWBALL NEPHEWS WERE GREEK SOLDIERS AT TROY

SHUT UP

YOU, SHUT UP!

"I CAN'T TAKE ANYONE IN MY FAMILY OUT IN PUBLIC!"

Every family tree produces nuts. Remember what George Bernard Shaw stated, "If you cannot get rid of the family skeleton, you may as well make it dance."

ANOTHER WAY TO TELL WHEN YOU'RE DEALING WITH SOMEONE WHO'S NOT PICKING UP ON THE BODY LANGUAGE

DID YOU WORK OUT YOUR LITTLE PROBLEM YET?

"HE'S SO CLUELESS, HOW CAN I GET THROUGH TO HIM?"

As the famous psychologist Kurt Lewin said, "If you want truly to understand something, try to change it." Since he is in another world, speak a different language. Try love letters, singing, or painting him a picture about what is important to you.

"MY DOCTOR CARES MORE ABOUT MONEY THAN ME!"

Learn to be a participant in your health care and not just a patient. Ask questions, write things down, and consult the Internet about your diagnosis. You can lead a horse to water, but you can't make him drink it. We all need to use a little horse sense.

"WHY DON'T WE EVER NOTICE THE DOOR IS OPEN?"

As Ralph Waldo Emerson stated, "Most of the shadows of this life are caused by our standing in our own sunshine." FBI and police officers have become more observant by practicing mindfulness meditation. Spend time meditating each day in order to see what is and what is not there!

"WE ARE NEVER ON THE SAME PAGE."

Fact: Everyone seems normal until you get to know
him or her. According to Mahatma Gandhi, "Honest
differences are often a healthy sign of progress."
Identify your differences and see how you compli-
ment one another.

"IS THIS ALL THERE IS?"

Remember what H.L.Mencken said, "You have two
choices in life: you can stay single and be miserable
or get married and wish you were dead." It is possible
to complain about not being married or about being
married. Imagine being happy first and then worry
about your relationship status.

"IS MY WIFE CRAZY, OR IS THERE SOME-THING TO MEDITATION?"

Is it crazy to want to be happy? According to the Dalai Lama, "The purpose of our existence is to seek happiness." Research shows that happiness is determined more by the state of our mind than by conditions, circumstances or events. Sit and breath deeply for 10 minutes each day to create a happy mind.

"I MARRIED A STUFFED SHIRT. I LOVE HIM, BUT HOW CAN I GET HIM TO DREAM?"

Worry less about your partner and keep dreaming yourself. As Maya Angelou states, "If one is lucky, a solitary fantasy can totally transform one million realities." Let your own happiness and joy transform him.

"SHE ALWAYS GETS TO DO WHAT SHE WANTS!"

Why not celebrate her ability to find joy wherever she is? FACT: All your happiness and all of your suffering are created by your mind. Replace jealousy with generosity and leave her a flower basket and a note of admiration. As Confucius said, "To hook up is joy."

JUST HOW STUPID DOES HE THINK I AM?

Remember, "sticks and stones may break your bones, but words will never hurt you." FACT: No matter how problematic the people in your life are, you are always the solution. Ignore the negative comments by doing something totally different.

"HIS ADDICTION TO BASEBALL INTER-FERES WITH EVERYTHING."

What is a "ground-rule double"? How about a "squeeze play"? If you know these, you have tried to appreciate his passion. If you haven't, you need to go to some more games. As Yogi Berra said, "You can observe a lot by watching." After all, it didn't become the National Pastime for nothing

"IT'S SO OBVIOUS, WHY WON'T HE JUST ADMIT IT?"

FACT: The Fifth Amendment of the US Constitution states that you don't have testify against yourself. Is it really necessary that he confess? Will it change your life? Let go of the urge to fix others and start to enjoy life more.

I NEVER SEE THINGS UNTIL IT IS TOO LATE.
According to Lou Holtz, "Life is ten percent what happens to me and ninety percent how I react to it." Remember that blind people can learn to live very satisfying lives. Focus on your behavior and not on how others score your performance.

"HE ALWAYS THINKS THIS WILL BE THE BIG IDEA THAT WILL CHANGE OUR LIFE."
As Mark Twain said, "The man with a new idea is a crank until the idea succeeds." Light bulbs, drive-through restaurants, and $5 cups of coffee were all laughed at...actually laughed at all the way to the bank! Start smiling. He may be right.

"I COMPLAIN ABOUT EVERYTHING....SEE, I'M DOING IT AGAIN!"

Complaining seldom changes anything other than your own feelings. As Dale Carnegie said: "Any fool can criticize, condemn and complain--and most do." As the Serenity Prayer states, you need to accept the things that cannot be changed.

"WE ALWAYS DANCED WHEN WE DATED, AND NOW HE RUNS WHEN THE MUSIC STARTS."

As the Polish proverb states, "The man who can't dance thinks the band is no good." Your husband needs to overcome his inhibitions and social anxieties. Arrange for dance lessons and get ready to dance with the stars!

"IS THE WHOLE WORLD ON A 'DUMB AND DUMBER' TRAIN?"

FACT: The average college graduate reads less than a book per year. What has happened to curiosity? As Albert Einstein said, "The important thing is not to stop questioning." Start a book club or reading circle with your friends and neighbors.

"EVERY GUY I DATE TURNS OUT TO BE MARRIED."

Maybe there is a message here? William James said, "If you care enough for the result, you will almost always achieve it." If your goal is to avoid marriage, you are batting a thousand! If your goal is a life-long partner, consider performing a background check on all future suitors.

"MY HUSBAND CARES MORE ABOUT THE DOG THAN ME!"

FACT: In every successful relationship there are five positive responses for every one negative. He must be getting more positives from the dog than you. Take a tip and make it your job to "out-do" the dog each day.

"OUR SON DOES EVERY GOOFY THING HIS FRIENDS DO...WHY CAN'T HE THINK FOR HIMSELF?"

Monkey see, monkey do. FACT: Peer pressure is a strong force that can be both positive and negative. Don't fight the concept, but use it to surround him with positive peer pressure. Invite kids over for a game night, or to a bowling party. Investigate other chances to create good karma!

ON THE EDGE

with Earl, Nadine & Weederman

BY JOE MARTIN & DR. JON CARLSON

GENERIC PORTRAIT OF WOMAN WITH FIVE OR MORE CHILDREN

"I'M LIKE A TIME-BOMB, THE SLIGHTEST THING SETS ME OFF."

Response patterns are learned early in life and seldom change. After the storm comes the calm. In the meantime, take a deep breath and count to ten slowly. Nowadays, they're calling it "meditation".

ON THE EDGE

with Earl, Nadine & Weederman

BY JOE MARTIN & DR. JON CARLSON

FINALIST: TATTOO YOU'RE MOST LIKELY TO HAVE SECOND THOUGHTS ABOUT COMPETITION

www.mrbof

"I'M THE ONLY ONE IN THE HOUSE WITHOUT A TATTOO OR A RING IN MY NOSE."

Every generation has its trademark. Yours was long hair and bell-bottoms. As Mark Twain said, "When I was fourteen, my father was so ignorant I could hardly stand to have the old man around. When I got to be twenty-one, I was astonished at how much the old man had learned in seven years."

"WHERE DO I GO TO GIVE UP?"

You are not alone. If there were somewhere to go when life seems hopeless, the line would be enormous. The noted psychiatrist R.D.Laing said, "Madness need not be all breakdown, it may also be breakthrough." Think of it as a fresh start and take advantage of it.

"WHAT AM I? CHOPPED LIVER?"

As Ralph Waldo Emerson said, "Make the most of yourself for that's all there is to you." Try a new hair color, wardrobe, or cologne. If that doesn't work, megaphones, skywriting and billboards could be your way to notoriety.

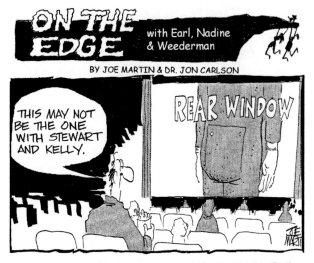

ON THE EDGE

with Earl, Nadine & Weederman

BY JOE MARTIN & DR. JON CARLSON

"CAN'T SHE EVER PICK A GOOD MOVIE?"

In most relationships, there is a partner who is in charge of entertainment. This leads to one feeling burdened and the other left out. Share the load; the goal is TWO thumbs up!

ON THE EDGE

with Earl, Nadine & Weederman

BY JOE MARTIN & DR. JON CARLSON

"MY WIFE IS HER OWN WORST ENEMY - SHE WON'T REST."

We make our own prisons. We set schedules and create obligations that lock us into unhappy situations. Break away, the world won't crumble! Start by following the rule of "No work after 7 PM", which has changed many of my client's lives.

"HE IS HEADED FOR SOME SERIOUS TROUBLE AND I CAN'T GET THROUGH TO HIM."
Most troubles come from facing problems too late.
Unfortunately some people have to learn the hard way.
As the English proverb says, "We never know the
worth of water until the well is dry." This is another
one that should go on the refrigerator.

ON THE EDGE
with Earl, Nadine & Weederman

BY JOE MARTIN & DR JON CARLSON

"MY WIFE IS ALWAYS SAYING THINGS THAT MAKE ME WONDER IF SHE IS COMMITTED TO ME."
She may be throwing things out to see if you are lis-
tening or even care. But, as Stanislaus I, King of
Poland, stated, "To believe with certainty, we must
begin with doubting." At times, we all are unsure of
our relationships, otherwise we would be complacent.
She is looking for reassurance, so give it to her.

"HE IS ALWAYS SO DEFENSIVE AND FOOLISH, BUT I CAN'T CONVINCE HIM OTHERWISE."

According to H. L.Mencken, "The penalty for laughing in a courtroom is six months in jail; if it were not for the penalty, the jury would never hear the evidence." Criticism is hard to take, even from a friend, relative or a perfect stranger. Next time he becomes defensive, focus on listening. As the old adage says, "If you give him enough rope, he'll hang himself."

"LAST 4th OF JULY, MY SON-IN-LAW MADE A LAUGHING STOCK OF HIMSELF AND NOW HE WON'T FACE ANYBODY IN THE FAMILY. HOW DO I GET TO SEE MY DAUGHTER AGAIN?"

Too often people wait and the problem grows - they should take action! "If the mountain won't come to Mohammed, then bring the mountain to him." Bake a cake, round up the gang, and get over there.

ON THE EDGE
with Earl, Nadine & Weederman
BY JOE MARTIN & DR. JON CARLSON

CLIFF DIVER WITH A RUBBER HEAD

"IT SEEMS SO EASY FOR MY CO-WORK-ERS, BUT EVERY DAY'S A STRUGGLE FOR ME."

As Confucius said, "Choose a job you love, and you will never work another day in your life." They say everybody has talent and excels at one special thing. Find yours, even if it isn't so obvious as a rubber head!

ON THE EDGE
with Earl, Nadine & Weederman
BY JOE MARTIN & DR. JON CARLSON

" WOULD YOU LIKE THIS TO BE THE SMOKING OR THE NON-SMOKING SECTION ? "

"HOW COME PEOPLE STILL SMOKE IN RESTAURANTS?

According to Barry Farber, "Crime expands according to our willingness to put up with it." The squeaky wheel seems to get the oil and we have been too silent and tolerant. Next time this happens indicate to the owner that in the future you will be eating in a non- smoking facility, and hope he responds with more than a drive-up window.

"HOW DO I MAKE AN INSANELY STUBBORN PERSON KNOW THAT HE IS WRONG?"

TWO tips: First be sure that you are not the insanely stubborn one! As the saying goes, "When arguing with a stupid person, be sure he isn't doing the same thing." Second: show this to your friend, and maybe he'll think about the price of winning all arguments.

"SHE ALWAYS HAS TO HAVE THE LAST WORD."

According to Eva Gabor, "Love is a game that two can play and both win." Rather than deciding what is best for you or your wife, start solving disagreements by asking what is best for "US"!

BY JOE MARTIN & DR. JON CARLSON

"WE'VE BEEN DOWN EVER SINCE OUR BUSINESS WENT DOWN!"

The biggest D is depression. According to Geoffrey Norman, "A lot of what passes for depression these days is nothing more than a body saying it needs work." Start taking antidepressants by developing your next business plan.

BY JOE MARTIN & DR. JON CARLSON

"I ANTICIPATE TROUBLE BUT NEVER ACT ON IT."

"You'll never plow a field by turning it over in your head." Fact: Anticipation requires taking action, and not simply predicting the future. Put some legs into your thoughts by doing one thing before breakfast that will change the outcome of the morning.

SIMPLE SOLUTIONS TO COMPLEX PROBLEMS

BILLS

"I DIDN'T KNOW THEY COULD LOCK YOU AWAY FOR NOT PAYING PARKING TICKETS."

It is time for you and your husband to take off your masks and face reality! Denial is always the easy way out. Start by answering the phone and opening your mail!!!

NUMBER ONE ON THE LIST OF THINGS THAT ONLY HAPPEN IN YOUR DREAMS

YOU'RE UP EARLY !

www.mrcolin.com

"MY HUSBAND THINKS IT'S OK TO STAY OUT ALL NIGHT WITH HIS CRONIES."

The other wives feel the same as you. Misery loves company. Get the women together and form your own support group - card night, theatre night. Have fun and maybe some time the two groups will get together for a mixer.

"MY SON IS 30, STILL AT HOME, AND ALL HE DOES IS TAKE UP SPACE."
As Confucius said, "It is better to light one small candle, than to curse the darkness." Think small. Set up some daily responsibilities - he can either do them or leave. Your kindness is not helping either of you.

"HE NEVER DOES WHAT HE SAYS HE'S GOING TO DO!"
Many a man is as good as his word, but his word is no good. As the Russian proverb states, "Don't put it in my ear, but in my hand." Relationships are only good when agreements are kept. Ask him to do something that is important to the running of the house, and no matter how long it takes, let him do it.

"MY HUSBAND DOESN'T MAKE A MOVE WITHOUT HIS MOTHER'S APPROVAL."

Family therapists use the word "enmeshment" to describe when a person is too close to their family. When you are too connected to your parents, you become too detached from your partner! Find some balance, take your wife out to lunch for a change.

"EVERYONE COMPLAINS ABOUT MY COOKING. YOU'D THINK I WAS THE WORLD'S WORST COOK."

As Simone Weil states, "We see the same colors, we hear the same sounds, but not in the same way." Be aware of the variety of ways that people prepare food. What is one person's delight might be another's torture. Consider a few new recipes along with your standard fare, and see if your popularity improves. Maybe one day each week your husband might want to be guest chef!

"EVERY MEMORIAL DAY OUR FAMILIES GET TOGETHER AND ALL THEY DO IS FIGHT."

As the Chinese proverb states, "Dig a well before you are thirsty." Chaos is calmed through structure and planning. Limit the time of your gathering and plan lots of noncompetitive games, and don't forget the keg of non-alcoholic beer for the cool down!

"IS IT WRONG TO WANT TO BE A COUPLE AGAIN, EVEN FOR JUST AN HOUR?!!

FACT: Today's marriages are too child-centered and not enough couple-centered. Move your relationship up the priority chart and not only add more fun to your life, but teach your children the importance of taking time for your marriage. Learn to do this with a guilt-free conscience. Your kids will not only survive, they will prosper.

"MY HUSBAND THRIVES ON PUTTING PEOPLE DOWN. HIS FAVORITE SAYING IS, 'ANYBODY CAN DO THAT!'"

As Bern Williams said, "A friend is a lot of things, but a critic he isn't." He should remember, "Don't belittle, be big", and help others to feel competent. You might try getting him a Don Rickles album and see if he doesn't recognize himself.

"WHY CAN'T I STAY MOTIVATED?"

As the old adage says, "The road to hell is paved with good intentions." Stay motivated by tailoring your new knowledge to your work setting. How? Immediately apply the new knowledge. Set your watch to beep each hour and make sure you have done something new between signals.

"MY WIFE NEVER TELLS ME BAD NEWS. I DIDN'T KNOW THE ELECTRIC BILL WASN'T PAID UNTIL THE LIGHTS WENT OFF."

FACT: Withholding bad news doesn't spare pain, but actually increases it. It is bad enough not to have money, but now you have a partner you can't trust! The truth often hurts, but so does being in the dark. As the Persian proverb states, "The man who speaks the truth is always at ease." Put your cards on the table, and don't be surprised when you are the winner. What I am saying is, GO ALL IN.

"PEOPLE TALK ABOUT GETTING TO FIRST OR SECOND BASE; I CAN'T EVEN GET A SECOND DATE."

As Denis Healy said, "When you are in a hole, stop digging." You need to lighten up and create a sense of humor. Fact: Women are attracted to men who are funny, spontaneous, and make them feel good about themselves. Remember, a good line is the shortest distance between two dates.

"I NEED THE DAY OFF, BUT I KNOW THEY WON'T GIVE IT TO ME IF I TELL THE TRUTH."

As Mark Twain said, "When in doubt, tell the truth." Fact: Honesty is the best policy (even if there are too few policy holders.) Living by your values, and not reacting to other people, will lead to long-term happiness, with or without the day off!!!

"MY EMPLOYEES SEEM OBLIVIOUS TO EVERYTHING AROUND THEM. WHAT CAN I DO?"

A smile in giving honest criticism can make the difference between resentment and reform. Share with your employees the immortal words of Andrew Carnegie, "The average person puts only 25% of his energy and ability into his work. The world takes off its hat to those who put in more than 50% of their capacity, and stands on its head for those few-and-far-between souls who devote 100 %." Let him know you are standing on your feet with your hat on!!!

"MY CHILD DOES POORLY ON TESTS, MAINLY BECAUSE HE DOESN'T READ DIRECTIONS."

Experience teaches you to recognize a mistake when you've made it again. As Muhammad Ali states, "Inside of a ring or out, ain't nothing wrong with going down. It's staying down that's wrong." Ask your child what he plans to do about his reading omissions and then make sure he follows through on his plan.

"MY HUSBAND GOES OUT OF HIS WAY TO IRRITATE ME! IT'S LIKE HE WANTS TO START A FIGHT."

As Hugh Allen put it, "There's a bit of ancient wisdom that appeals to us: it's a saying that a fight starts only with the second blow." No response is better than a negative one. Consider tuning out your husband until he discovers kindness. Don't expect things to be better in the morning. This will take a while.

ON THE EDGE

with Earl, Nadine & Weederman

BY JOE MARTIN & DR. JON CARLSON

MAN IN "EASY-GRIP" HAT DEMONSTRATING MOST HUMILIATING WAY TO TRAVEL

"WHAT'S THE DEAL WITH AIRPORT SECURITY? WE'RE SUPPOSED TO BE CUSTOMERS, NOT CATTLE."

Travel enlarges the minds of some people, but swells the heads of others. Fact: We can have too much of a good thing, but it probably will not go away. Next time airport security humbles you, remember the words of Confucius, "To be wronged is nothing unless you continue to remember it."

ON THE EDGE

with Earl, Nadine & Weederman

BY JOE MARTIN & DR. JON CARLSON

A BIG PART OF THE REASON WHY IT'S IMPORTANT TO READ THE SMALL PRINT

TILL DEATH DO US PART !?

JOE MARTIN

"AFTER ONE DATE, MY DAUGHTER WANTS TO GET MARRIED."

Love at first sight might be right. Remember, the fun is not in getting married, but in getting to marriage. Fact: Marriage experts recommend that you date long enough to experience all four seasons. Slow down the process and enjoy the ride. Don't forget what Rodney Dangerfield said, "My wife and I were happy for twenty years. Then we met."

"I THINK HAVING A BABY IS A PRIVATE AFFAIR, BUT MY HUSBAND WANTS TO MAKE A BIG PRODUCTION OF IT - LIKE HE'S SPIELBERG!"

Fact: Boundaries and privacy are important in families. The Irish proverb states, "The three most beautiful sights: a potato garden in bloom, a ship in sail, a woman after the birth of her child." This is a moment to experience and not to memorialize. Tell him you really want him to participate in the delivery, but only if he can get through the metal detector.

"WE WERE ALL PALS, NOW I'M SUPERVISOR AND EATING LUNCH ALL BY MYSELF."

As Bette Midler said, "The worst part about success is trying to find someone who is happy for you." It is not necessary to eat alone, just because you have been promoted. Order pizza each Friday and invite them on up for some laughs.

"MY HUSBAND STARES DUMBFOUNDED AT EVERY PRETTY GIRL. IS IT OK TO CLOBBER HIM?"

No, its really not his fault. Fact: Men are "hard-wired" to look at pretty girls. Instinct is to look for a partner that will provide the man the best offspring. Just because he has a partner he loves doesn't stop the genetic programming. As Carl Jung said, "One must be able to let things happen."

"OUR BEST FRIENDS' WHOLE LIVES RE-VOLVE AROUND THE WHIMS OF THEIR PET! IS THAT NORMAL?"

Not only is it normal, it might be preferable!! According to George Elliot, "Animals are such agreeable friends - they ask no questions, they pass no criticisms." Fact: Even with their few "whims", they are less maintenance and provide more respect than an average teenager. Try taking your cat out for dinner(!?)

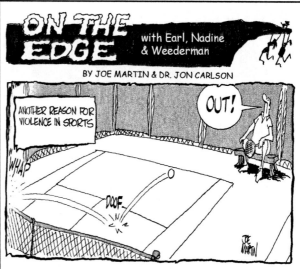

"MY BOYFRIEND CAN'T PLAY A GAME WITHOUT CHEATING!"

As Homer Simpson says, "Cheating is the gift man gives himself." Fact: He who will cheat at play, will cheat you any way. Let him know that any further cheating will result in an immediate disqualification!

"I'M AFRAID OF DOCTORS AND EVERY TIME I GET UP THE COURAGE TO GO TO ONE, I READ SOME HOSPITAL HORROR STORY."

According to Anton Chekhov, "Doctors are just the same as lawyers; the only difference is that lawyers merely rob you, whereas doctors rob and kill you too." Don't be afraid to get medical help, but don't do it blindly. Ask questions. Insist on clear explanations, and if appropriate, second and third opinions.

"MY HUSBAND WON'T WEAR HIS SEATBELT."

He has a bad habit but so do you! He knows all the reasons to
wear seatbelts but nobody is going to tell him what to do.
You need to quit hassling him. Sometimes you just have to
accept things even if they are not very acceptable. In time,
the "Click it or ticket" campaign will have its way with him!

"MY HUSBAND CAN'T FIX ANYTHING WITHOUT MAKING IT WORSE."

"Give him the right tools and pretty soon the leaky faucet becomes a running stream." It's important to know your limits!
In the case of your husband, he is able to repair things only to
the best of his inability. Why not give him a gift certificate at
the local Rent-A-Real-Fix-It-Person store for Father's Day?
Think of all the money you'll save.

"IS IT POSSIBLE TO BE A NATURAL BORN LOSER?"
Psychologists believe that some people have personalities that keep them from being successful. You are
not "born a failure" but have actually learned to
pursue failure with your bad attitude and lack of effort.
FACT: Anyone who can find success as a failure can
find success in other areas.

**"I CAME UP WITH THE IDEA, I IMPLEMENTED IT...
THEN MY BOSS GOT PROMOTED! WHAT'S THE DEAL?"**
The good news is that bad deeds always catch up with
people....you reap what you sow. In business, the Peter Principle applies, "people are promoted to their level of incompe-
tence." In the meantime, enjoy the fact that you have good
ideas and have been able to bring about a significant change.
It's just a matter of time before you will get to test the Peter
Principle!!!

"INFOMERCIALS ARE PUTTING US IN THE POOR HOUSE."

As Oscar Wilde said, "I can resist everything except temptation." Infomercials tempt us with the possibility of perfect thighs, hairless noses, and the formula for becoming a millionaire by next Tuesday. Say no to temptation by doing a media fast for two months and watch your bottom line soar!

"WHY DO I DO THE CRAZY THINGS I DO?"

As the English proverb says, "Stupidity won't kill you, but it can make you sweat." Stop battling with yourself in order to avoid responsibilities!! Join forces with yourself and tackle things like getting a job, finding a partner, and painting the house. Fact: Those who battle themselves will lose as many times as they win.

"WHY CAN'T I STOP GAMBLING? I NEVER WIN!"
Fact: We are creatures of habit and tend to do the same things even if they are not rewarding or satisfying. As the Spanish proverb states, "Habits are at first cobwebs and then cables." You need to break out of your pattern by gambling less frequently, for shorter time, and with less money. Many people also find support at Gambling Anonymous (GA) meetings.

"I ALWAYS DEPENDED ON MY PARENTS FOR ADVICE, BUT NOW THAT I HAVE MY OWN FAMILY, I FIND WE DON'T ALWAYS AGREE."
According to John Finley, "Maturity is the capacity to endure uncertainty." You are going through a normal life "passage". Fact: Children must grow up and individuate from their parents. Thank your parents for taking you this far, but now you are going to drive yourself.

ON THE EDGE

with Earl, Nadine & Weederman

BY JOE MARTIN & DR. JON CARLSON

"MAYBE YOU SHOULD TRY THE ONE WITH THE CLOWN ON IT"

"I CAN'T DO THE THINGS I USED TO DO. I THOUGHT 60 WAS SUPPOSED TO BE THE NEW 40."

Focus on what's right, not on what's wrong. It's what you can do that matters. In my 30's, I took third in U.S. Cross Country, now I can't run at all. The elliptical machine is my new highway.

ON THE EDGE

with Earl, Nadine & Weederman

BY JOE MARTIN & DR. JON CARLSON

"IT'S OK .. I'M WATCHING HIM"

"ARE TODAY'S PARENTS TOO LENIENT? THEY SEEM TO LET THEIR KIDS RUN EVERYWHERE."

"Spare the rod and spoil the child." Parenting requires both kindness and firmness. Most parents are kind but need to be firm and say "NO". Fact: Children (and even teens) want parents to say "NO" and set limits. Find some courage and provide some guidance by saying "NO" three times to your child today!!

"MY HUSBAND BROODS AND GIVES ME THE SILENT TREATMENT TO GET HIS WAY...HOW CAN I COMBAT THIS ANNOYING TACTIC?

Fact: Stonewalling is one of the four ways to ruin a marriage. Usually when stonewalling is present so are criticism, defensiveness, and contempt. One way to reduce his pouting is for you to remove the criticism and contempt that drive him away.

"MY FRIEND IS WAY TOO VINDICTIVE WHEN THINGS DON'T GO HIS WAY."

FACT: "The end never justifies the meanness." As Chokyi Nyima Rinpoche stated, "Every thing has to do with attitude." Help your friend by returning kindness for hurt. Maintain your positive attitude as a way to help him find his.

"WHAT CAN I DO TO REMEMBER THINGS? IS THERE A TRICK TO IMPROVING MEMORY?"

According to Mark Twain, "It isn't so astonishing the number of things that I can remember, as the number of things I can remember that aren't so." Memory aids really do work. Try writing things down, making lists, using post-it notes, as well as reading "The Memory Book" for more ideas.

"I WRECK EVERYTHING I TOUCH."

Mark Twain stated, "A man who carries a cat by the tail learns something he can learn in no other way." Hopefully you have learned that your path of destruction will only stop once you get off of it. Use your skills at making friends with a "Bob the Builder" kind of person.

"MY WIFE THINKS SHE IS THE WORLD'S AUTHOR-ITY ON CHILD PSYCHOLOGY BECAUSE EVERY WEEK SHE READS A NEW BOOK ON THE SUBJECT."
Let your wife know that "Professionals built the Titanic--amateurs the Ark." You have just as much right (maybe not knowledge) to guide your children. Maybe it is time to pull together and increase both of your *Parenting IQ's!!!*

"HOW CAN I GET MY CHILDREN TO RESPECT ME?"
As J.B.Priestly stated, "There was no respect for youth when I was young, and now I am old, there is no respect for age - I missed it coming and going." FACT: Giving respect is the best way to get it. Begin to listen to your children, value their opinions, and allow them to make decisions. In a short time **you will think** you are royalty!

"MY HUSBAND AND I BOTH COME FROM LARGE FAMILIES. DO I HAVE TO INVITE EVERYONE EVERY TIME I HAVE AN EVENT?"

"Etiquette is the right way to do a wrong thing." It is important to use tact and diplomacy. Let everyone know that you have space limitations and can't be as inclusive as you would like. Emphasize that everyone is important and loved, even if they can only be invited to every third event.

"HOW CAN I STOP MY FAMILY FROM TRYING TO HELP?"

As John Updike states, "All blessings are mixed blessings." Let your family know that you appreciate their efforts however it would be best if they work in areas where mistakes are more forgiving. Perhaps the basement, garage, backyard or somewhere else out of sight would be a good place to contribute?

"MY WIFE LOOKS AT THE WORLD THROUGH ROSE-COLORED GLASSES AND SUGARCOATS EVERYTHING. AM I A STICK-IN-THE-MUD?"
A relationship is a lot like a teeter-totter. If your partner is too optimistic, you are probably a stick-in-the-mud. As you get out of the mud, her vision will change. You need to remove the word "NO" from your vocabulary when your wife asks you to do something. Take a walk with her on the sunny side of the street!!

"WHY AM I ALWAYS THE ONE WHO GETS STUCK?"
FACT: "You can always tell a fool, unless he's hiding inside of you." Discover the signals that tell others that it is OK to "stick you". End your victim lifestyle by speaking up. Remember what Leo Tolstoi said, "We lost because we told ourselves we lost."

"I HAVE A FIVE-YEAR-OLD WHO NEVER STOPS ASKING QUESTIONS...I'M NOT COMPLAINING BUT DOES HE REALLY WANT TO KNOW ALL THESE THINGS?"

Fact: Children who ask questions in a "rapid fire" fashion do not care about the answers. Your son wants you to notice and pay attention to him! Try ignoring him when he is demanding your involvement. Later when he is acting appropriately, come to him with friendly questions and stories.

"I MARRIED AN IDIOT...I HAVE TO MAKE EVERY DECISION AND I'M GETTING TIRED OF MAKING ALL THE DECISIONS."

As Rupert Murdoch stated, "Problems come when the individual tries to hand over the decision making to a committee." Fact: It may be easier to accept the situation than to change it. Decison-making is better kept away from your partner, so focus instead on other ways that he can be responsible. Remember, every captain needs a crew!

"MY FRIENDS AND I ALL THINK WE ARE TURNING INTO OUR MOTHERS. DOES EVERYONE GO THROUGH THIS STAGE? WILL MY DAUGHTER BE THINKING THIS WAY WHEN SHE IS AN ADULT?"

Fact: Research shows that we model our lives after one or both parents. Be sure your daughter won't bemoan this fact! Create a liability "short list" and begin the metamorphosis. Remember the Latin proverb, "Times change and we change with them."

"MY HUSBAND IS FOREVER GETTING ME UP IN THE MIDDLE OF THE NIGHT WITH HIS PROBLEMS!"

"Don't get annoyed if your neighbor plays his stereo at two o'clock in the morning. Call him at four and tell him how much you enjoyed it." According to Edward Somers, "Every problem contains within itself the seeds of its own solution." Set your alarm and share some of your troubles.

ON THE EDGE

with Earl, Nadine & Weederman

BY JOE MARTIN & DR. JON CARLSON

"MY SON EXPECTS TO BE REWARDED FOR EVERYTHING HE DOES...."

Whatever happened to Ralph Waldo Emerson's famous saying, "The reward of a thing well done is to have done it."? FACT: Children need to learn to reward themselves for satisfying work. Let your son know he really helps the family when he pitches in. Tell him often that you appreciate his cooperation and all that he does.

ON THE EDGE

with Earl, Nadine & Weederman

BY JOE MARTIN & DR. JON CARLSON

"STILL NO WORD FROM MOTOWN ?"

"WE HAVE 'CALL-WAITING' BUT WHEN MY DAUGHTER IS EXPECTING A CALL NO ONE'S ALLOWED TO USE THE PHONE (WE'VE TAKEN HER CELL PHONE AWAY)."

As Fran Leibowitz stated, "Remember that as a teenager you are at the last stage in your life when you will be happy to hear that the phone is for you." Having friends and staying connected is an important task of adolescence. Fact: **Some problems are best not solved!** Make your calls when your daughter is gone, which will increase with each day passing.

"MY HUSBAND IS VERY COMPETITIVE BUT HE IS ALSO A VERY FREQUENT AND VERY POOR LOSER. HELP!!"

"Some people are good losers, and others can't act." With the help of Vince Lombardi, winning has become everything. Remind your husband to follow George Meredith's advice, "Always imitate the behavior of the winners when you lose."

"I ABSOLUTELY HATE MY HUSBAND'S FAVORITE RESTAURANT AND IT'S A FAMILY RITUAL TO GO THERE ON SATURDAY NIGHT."

As Lucretius stated, "What is food to one is to another bitter poison." Fact: Rituals are important for families but only as long as they bind *everyone* together. Leave your regular Saturday night routine at least once per month and have fun co-constructing the new custom together.

"MY BOYFRIEND IS VERY SECRETIVE ABOUT WHERE HE WORKS AND LIVES. I DON'T EVEN KNOW HIS PHONE NUMBER...COULD HE BE MARRIED?"

John Dryden said, "Secrets are edged tools and must be kept from children and from fools." Stop being a fool! Men who insist on this type of secret relationship are not able to have a satisfying partnership. Normally there are two sides to every story, but not here! Change your phone number and look for greener pastures.

"I HAVE TO FIRE SOMEONE I'VE KNOWN FOR 20 YEARS. IS THERE ANY NICE WAY TO DO THIS?"

As Yogi Berra stated, "I don't want to make the wrong mistake." FACT: There are no nice ways to fire somebody you have known for twenty years. The better ways involve honesty, truth and compassion.

"HOW MANY CHANCES DO YOU GIVE SOMEONE WHO IS CONSTANTLY LETTING YOU DOWN?"
It depends on how much you want to suffer. As Boyle Roche stated, "Disappointment is the nurse of wisdom." Since you are asking, the time has come for "Last Call". Practice detachment and let them know you are moving on.

"MY HUSBAND AND I HAVE NEVER BEEN VERY ATHLETIC-WE'D LIKE TO BE A BETTER INFLUENCE ON THE KIDS."
As Ralph Waldo Emerson said, "Always do what you are afraid to do." Fact: It is best to lead by example. Pick a sport and demonstrate the daily discipline and long-term commitment needed for happiness and success. Any sport will do and the list of possibilities is long: horseshoes, badminton, speed walking, bowling, karate....

ON THE EDGE with Earl, Nadine & Weederman

BY JOE MARTIN & DR. JON CARLSON

"ON THE OTHER HAND IT'S KIND OF REFRESHING TO DEAL WITH A PROBLEM THAT HAS NOTHING TO DO WITH CASH FLOW"

"ALL WE TALK ABOUT IS MONEY PROBLEMS."

"Money is a good servant but a bad master." You need to talk about other things too. Limit your talk about money problems to one hour each week. This will not only help you get along better, but according to Harvard Professor Herbert Bensen, will create a fresh perspective that will lead to a "breakthrough" in your money crisis.

ON THE EDGE with Earl, Nadine & Weederman

BY JOE MARTIN & DR. JON CARLSON

"I THINK WE CAN ALL AGREE THAT INCREASING PORTERFIELD'S VACATIONS HAS BEEN, AT BEST, ONLY A TEMPORARY SOLUTION"

"MY HUSBAND WON'T RETIRE BECAUSE HE THINKS THE COMPANY WILL FALL APART WITHOUT HIM."

Fact: All men believe they are important. As Malcolm Muggeridge says, "Few men of action have been able to make a graceful exit at the appropriate time." Help him find importance in other areas of his life. Be sure and tell him how much you are looking forward to his being home full-time!!

ON THE EDGE

with Earl, Nadine & Weederman

BY JOE MARTIN & DR. JON CARLSON

LOANS

"THEY'RE GETTING THE HIGH-PRESSURE HOSE OUT...
LOOKS LIKE ANOTHER 'NO' "

"MY EX-HUSBAND HAS TOTALLY RUINED MY CREDIT RATING, NEVER PAID ME A DIME, MADE IT IMPOSSIBLE TO RAISE MY DAUGHTER, AND NOW HE WANTS TO GIVE HER AWAY AT THE WEDDING!"

"Pain is inevitable. Suffering is optional." Remember what Ralph Waldo Emerson said, "It is the wounded oyster that mends its shell with a pearl." Your ex will only be as much trouble to you as you allow. Let your daughter know that it is *her* wedding and she can choose the cast of characters.

ON THE EDGE

with Earl, Nadine & Weederman

BY JOE MARTIN & DR. JON CARLSON

www.mrboffo.com

MOST WRONG AWARD

IS THAT YOU DWINKY TINKY?!

"WHY DO I ALWAYS MAKE THE WRONG CHOICES?"

A s Oliver Goldsmith stated, "People seldom improve when they have no other model but themselves to copy after." Fact: People with self-defeating personalities are their own worst enemy!! Therefore, if something makes sense to you, then do the opposite; for starters, whenever you feel like talking, leave the room!!!

ON THE EDGE

with Earl, Nadine & Weederman

BY JOE MARTIN & DR. JON CARLSON

THE DOG WHO HATED HUGS AND THE CAT WHO LOVED TO GIVE THEM

"MY HUSBAND CAN'T DEAL WITH ANY KIND OF PUBLIC AFFECTION."

According to Elayne Boosler, "I know what men want. Men want to be really, really close to someone who will leave them alone." Get close to your husband by giving him the space in public he requests. My guess is that it will pay big dividends when the doors are shut and public is gone!

ON THE EDGE

with Earl, Nadine & Weederman

BY JOE MARTIN & DR. JON CARLSON

"MY WIFE IS PERMANENTLY ATTACHED TO HER COMPUTER."

As the Finnish proverb states, "Happiness is a place between too much and too little." Buddhists talk about "attachments to things" as being the source of suffering. Fact: Many people overdo things to avoid others. Bring her out of her "cyber-hiding"! Offer her a computer-free weekend in Paris!

"I CAN'T DO ANYTHING WITHOUT MY HUSBAND PUTTING IN HIS TWO CENTS."

Fact: We all want to feel valued and to believe we are important as a partner. As Kelly Smith said, "I want my husband to take me in his arms and whisper those three little words that all women long to hear, 'You were right.'" Let your husband know that there is no bigger turn-on!!

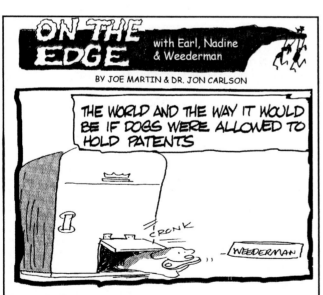

"OUR DOG TELLS US WHEN IT'S TIME TO GET UP, GO TO SLEEP, AND WHEN TO EAT. IT USED TO BE CUTE, BUT NOW IT'S STARTING TO GET OLD!"

Troubles are like babies - they grow larger if you nurse them. The dog has gone from trainee to trainer. Before calling the Dog Whisperer, remember what Harry Truman said, "I never take a problem to bed with me at night." Begin using a kennel for your dog each evening. With each bark, move it further out of hearing range.

"I'M ALWAYS ON THE GO, I NEVER GET A BREAK. IS THAT NORMAL?"

According to Oscar Wilde, "Whenever a man does a thoroughly stupid thing, it is always from the noblest motives." Fact: Constant "moving" will result in burnout or a flaming crash. You need to break this pattern. Here is your project: set aside an hour each day to work hard doing absolutely nothing!

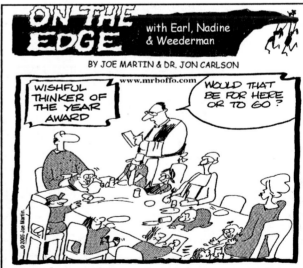

'I CAN'T TAKE MY KIDS ANYWHERE; THEY'RE LIKE WILD ANIMALS.'

As Homer Simpson stated, "When I look at the smiles on all the children's faces, I just know they're about to jab me with something." Fortunately, they are trainable. Use positive peer pressure. Have them invite a "well-mannered" friend along the next time you go to dinner. Watch "good overcome evil" as the positive model influences your kids.

"ALL MY KIDS WANT TO DO IS BREAK THINGS!"
As Martin Mull states, "Having children is like having a bowling alley in your brain." There will be lots of crashes until your child learns to control both *coordination* and *curiosity*. For at least the next 20 years, pack up the china and other breakables, and designate the basement as the place for "demolition derby".

"HOW CAN I KEEP THE HOUSE CLEAN WITHOUT WHINING AND COMPLAINING ALL DAY?"
"God made dirt, so dirt don't hurt." As Phyllis Diller stated, "Cleaning the house before your kids are done growing is like shoveling the walk before it stops snowing." Lower your expectations and watch your sanity return!!

"MY HUSBAND JUST GOT LAID OFF, HASN'T BEEN IN THE JOB MARKET IN 20 YEARS, AND KEEPS MAKING UP EXCUSES TO AVOID GOING ON INTERVIEWS."

Fact: Fear of any additional failure can paralyze. As Vauvenargues said, "There are those who are so scrupulously afraid of doing wrong, they seldom venture to do anything." You can help him through encouragement and helping him realize the many things he has been successful at, such as twenty years of marriage!

"I WAS REPLACED BY A COMPUTER ON MY LAST TWO JOBS - WHAT IS HAPPENING?"

As Heraclitus observed thousands of years ago, "Everything flows and nothing stays....You can't step twice in the same river." You need to learn to get used to life's inevitable changes. You have already learned to adapt to the $5 cup of coffee and the $20,000 car, now you need to make the next leap as you locate your next paycheck.

"WE'VE GOT TO DO SOMETHING ABOUT THESE ANSWERING MACHINES!"

As Sandra Bernhard stated, "Personally I'm waiting for caller IQ." It is not the machines but the people who misuse them. If you use an answering machine, return all calls within 24 hours or suggest an alternate way to reach you. We also "second" Alicia Brandt, "The technological advance I wish I could get is an addition for my answering machine. a Get-to-the-Point button.."

"MY HUSBAND HAS STARTED A SMALL MICRO-BREWERY WITH HIS BROTHER AND THAT'S ALL HE TALKS ABOUT."

As the Chinese proverb states, "Everything is difficult at first." It is really important to your husband to be successful. Support his efforts by showing regular appreciation for his efforts and entrepreneur spirit, and in no time he will again be curious about your world.

"I TRY TO ORGANIZE MY FAMILY. I SET A SCHEDULE OF RESPONSIBILITIES BUT NO ONE FOLLOWS IT!"

Don't give up. As the Russian proverb states, "Without a shepherd, sheep are not a flock." Try a more democratic style of leadership by having a family meeting and allowing everyone to participate in the splitting-up of the household tasks. Having a voice increases participation!!!

"ALL MY CHILDREN WANT TO DO IS FIGHT!"

As Ed Asner stated, "Raising kids is part joy and part guerilla warfare." Fighting is common in families where kids are either close together in age or where parents have underlying conflicts. You can't do anything about age differences but you can honestly look into what is going on in your marriage. See a couples' counselor for a check-up; it'll be worth the time and money!!

"ARE HOSPITALS AS DANGEROUS AS PEOPLE SAY?"
As Mark Twain said, "Be careful when reading health books; you may die of a misprint." Take responsibility if you have to go to a hospital. Just as we have said about doctor's visits, you need to be involved and aware. Ask others for their opinions and because you are "not well", have a trusted friend with you *at all times.* Don't forget, questioning can keep you alive!

"IS THERE ANYTHING NON-PHOTOGENIC PEOPLE CAN DO? I HAVE A CLASS REUNION COMING UP!"
As Mark Twain said, "Why do you sit there looking like an envelope without any address on it?" Fact: Attitude determines how good you will look. Begin by smiling at everyone. Next consider a new wardrobe (with tailoring), a cosmetic makeover, and maybe a few visits to the health club. Bottom line: accept the things that you can't change and change those you can--you'll look "MARVELOUS"!

ON THE EDGE

with Earl, Nadine & Weederman

BY JOE MARTIN & DR. JON CARLSON

ANOTHER WAY TO TELL WHEN YOU'RE DEALING WITH SOMEONE WHO NOW HAS A CLEAR UNDERSTANDING OF HIS POSITION IN THE HOUSEHOLD DECISION-MAKING PROCESS

FROM NOW ON I'M "COMMAND CENTRAL" AND YOU'RE "DINK THE DOPE"!

BILLS

www.mrboffo.com

"I SCREWED UP AND LOST EVERYTHING IN A DUMB BUSINESS DEAL. NOW MY WIFE'S TAKEN OVER EVERYTHING AND I'M JUST A BYSTANDER."

Your life sounds like Jean Kerr's, "I make mistakes; I'll be the second to admit it." As in baseball, you should get two more swings!! Flex your muscles by reminding your wife of the old cliché: "One swallow does not make a summer." Let her know that you plan to continue doing all the things you did before the setback.

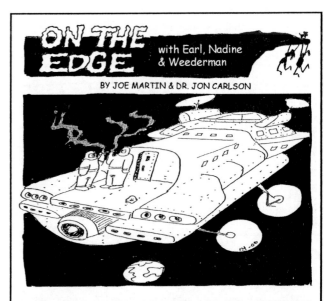

ON THE EDGE

with Earl, Nadine & Weederman

BY JOE MARTIN & DR. JON CARLSON

"HOW CAN I GET MY HUSBAND TO STOP SMOKING?"

As Dave Barry said, "Cigarette sales would drop to zero if the warning said, 'Cigarettes contain fat.'" Fact: You can't change for somebody else, but you can make his or her change worthwhile. Suggest he pick a **Quit Day.** Take the money spent on tobacco each day and put it in a jar. One year from the **Day,** plan to go on an exotic getaway!!

"WE LIVE IN A HIGH-RISE. MY HUSBAND BOUGHT A TELESCOPE, AND HE IS NOT LOOKING AT THE STARS! IS THIS AGAINST THE LAW?"

As Jason Love questioned, "Is Cupid blind or just sadistic?" Ogling the neighbors is not the road to marital happiness. You need to focus his attention and the telescope in the right direction. You could start by naming a star after him and making sure you find it together.

"I ALWAYS FEEL LIKE THE ODDBALL IN THE CROWD."

Sometimes people actually "belong" by being different and not fitting in. As Eric Hoffler said, "Man is most uniquely human when he turns obstacles into opportunities." What can you do to capitalize on your ODD-ness? Make your liabilities into assets. Make your hair even bluer, your clothes baggier, and turn your hat in a different direction.

"EVER SINCE OUR IN-LAWS LOANED US MONEY FOR A DOWNPAYMENT ON OUR HOUSE, IT'S ALL THEY TALK ABOUT."

As P.J. O'Rourke stated, "Family love is messy, clinging, and of an annoying and repetitive pattern, like bad wallpaper." Pay back the money as quickly as possible, and in the future use a mortgage broker.

"MY HUSBAND'S A DOCTOR. WE CAN'T GO TO A SOCIAL FUNCTION WITHOUT EVERYONE TREATING HIM LIKE HE'S A FREE CLINIC!"

As Mark Twain put it, "Few things are harder to put up with than a good example." Your husband was trained in medical school to say "NO" and keep boundaries. At some level he enjoys the attention and the ability to share *(maybe even show off)* his knowledge. Many of us choose medical careers because we like to be needed.

"MY FATHER-IN-LAW IS THE MOST TACTLESS PERSON IN THE WORLD - I'VE PUT UP WITH HIM FOR 20 YEARS!!

We tolerate differences of opinion in people that are close to us. As George E. Bergman said, "Tact is the art of making guests feel at home when that's really where you wish they were." Continue to follow the maxim: "If someone makes you sick, try to make them well." Keep doing what you are doing as you are too far down The Compassion Highway to change direction, and it's really not a bad road to follow!

"WHENEVER I WORRY, I EAT....IS THERE A BETTER SUBSTITUTE?"

According to Peter de Vries, "Gluttony is an emotional escape, a sign something is eating us." The hunger is a red flag indicating that you are struggling with a larger issue. Identify and solve the *real* problem, and then reward yourself with a banana split or two.

"WE FOUND OUT YESTERDAY THAT WE HAVE VIRTU-ALLY NOTHING TO RETIRE ON!"

This bad break may turn out for the best. Fact: Many people die or decline in health within 6 months of retirement. This will force you to remain active for many more years. Alex Comfort suggests, "Two weeks is about the ideal length of time to retire." Start planning your second careers and make sure you'll be doing something that you enjoy.

"I SLEEP ALL THE TIME - AND I LIKE IT!"

The Italian proverb states, "Five hours of sleep a traveler, seven a scholar, eight a merchant, and eleven every knave." Fact: When life is enjoyable, people need less sleep. Put some life into your waking hours by doing activites that are enjoyable for you. Start each day with 30 minutes of fun!

"NOTHING GOES ON IN OUR FAMILY WITHOUT EVERYONE BEING INVOLVED - EVEN THIRD COUSINS!"

As Henry David Thoreau said, "I would rather sit on a pumpkin and have it all to myself than be on a crowded velvet cushion." Fact: Healthy families need closeness, but also independence. Slowly begin to individuate by skipping a Sunday dinner, joining a bowling league, going shopping with friends, or any other activities that help you have your own identity as well as a family one.

"I THOUGHT ALL MY TROUBLES WOULD BE OVER IF I GOT ANOTHER JOB AND GOT OUT OF DEBT, BUT NOW THEY ARE WORSE."

As the French proverb states, "He that spends more than he is worth spins a rope for his own neck." Money isn't the problem, it is how you manage your money. You need to work on spending responsibly. Create a budget and mean it this time!!

"THE CHILDREN OF OUR FRIENDS AND RELATIVES ARE DRIVING OUR PETS CRAZY."

As was said on the television show *Ali McBeal*, "So here I am the victim of my own choices." Fact: Pets, like children, need protection, structure, and discipline. Place the animals OFF LIMITS when company comes to visit. Hook up the X-Box, get out the horseshoes, and provide other play outlets that don't lead to **pet abuse**.

"I WANT MY CHILDREN TO HAVE A FULL EDUCATION WITHOUT CENSORSHIP; I'M MEETING WITH A LOT OF OPPOSITION."

Don't be *over concerned* with other's opinions as you have the right to raise your children however you choose. But allowing them to read *Playboy* or having unlimited cable access shows laziness not thoughtfulness. As Antoine de Saint-Exupery stated, "To be a man is, precisely, to be responsible." Read books and watch programs with your kids to make sure their values are not distorted.

"I STARTED MY OWN BUSINESS AND IT SEEMS TO BE 'DOG EAT DOG' FOR SURVIVAL- IS THIS THE ONLY WAY?"

As Washington Allston states, "The only competition worthy of a wise man is with himself." Starting a new business is difficult, but how **you** do your new business is your choice. Remember that ability, breaks, and courage determine success. Stay away from the *dogfights* and concentrate on your business plan.

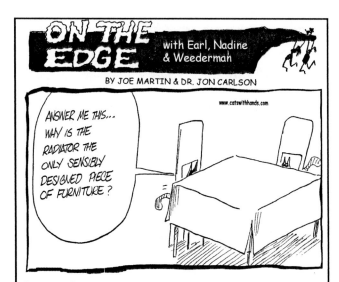

"I CAN'T FIT IN MY CAR AND I'M NOT THAT OVERWEIGHT."

As Ben Klitzner stated, "Middle age is when your narrow waist and broad mind begin to change places." Fact: Cars are smaller AND people are bigger. The auto industry is not going to change, so you will need to lose some weight to travel comfortably. Try to walk to as many places as possible until the car becomes your size!!

ON THE EDGE

with Earl, Nadine & Weederman

BY JOE MARTIN & DR. JON CARLSON

" THERE GO THE RUMOR MONGERS "

"WHENEVER ANYTHING HAPPENS IN MY LIFE, THE WHOLE BLOCK KNOWS ABOUT IT. IS THERE NO PRIVACY ANYMORE?"

As George Bernard Shaw states, "There is no satisfaction in hanging a man who does not object to it." What are you doing that makes such a good story? Learn how to fly under the radar, and start wearing camouflage whenever possible.

ON THE EDGE

with Earl, Nadine & Weederman

BY JOE MARTIN & DR. JON CARLSON

IF THE JUNGLE CAT HAD THE LOGIC, COMMON SENSE, STAMINA AND RESOURCES OF MAN

OK.... WE GAVE IT A SHOT... LET'S GO BACK TO THE CAVE AND CRACK OPEN A COUPLE OF CANS OF TUNA

"WHY ARE SOME PEOPLE BURNING WITH DESIRE TO ACCOMPLISH SOMETHING GREAT, WHILE I'M HAPPY DELIVERING THE MAIL?"

Aristotle stated, "All men seek one goal: success or happiness." You have found happiness, and don't let others' aspirations impact your satisfaction. Fact: The happiest people are those who are too busy to notice. You have added new meaning to the slogan "We Deliver"!!

"I HAVE A TEENAGE SON WHO CAN'T SEEM TO DO ANY-THING RIGHT, EVEN THE SIMPLEST CHORE--IS THIS HIS WAY OF GETTING OUT OF WORK?"
There's a good reason, and then there's the real reason! As James Thurber states, "You can fool too many of the people too much of the time." All behavior has a purpose, and his is to get you to do his work. Let him know that you are no longer doing his work without being paid overtime. Either he works, or you get to spend his allowance!

"MY HUSBAND USES ANY EXCUSE TO HAVE A PARTY.
Maybe he parties to get away from you? Fact: Men who do not feel valued tend to pull away from marriage. As Zsa Zsa Gabor states, "Husbands are like fires. They go out when un-attended." Make him feel important by planning social activi-ties with you that he will enjoy. Surprise him with tickets to the Monster Truck Rally or a NASCAR race. He'll have no reason to party!!!

ON THE EDGE with Earl, Nadine & Weederman

BY JOE MARTIN & DR. JON CARLSON

"IT'S SO EASY TO CRITICIZE OTHER PEOPLE... MAYBE THAT'S WHAT I'LL DO TODAY"

"I DON'T MIND DOING ALL THE WORK AROUND THE HOUSE, I ENJOY IT, ESPECIALLY THE COOKING. WHAT I DON'T LIKE IS THE CRITICISM."

As Elbert Hubbard says, "Happiness is a habit." Many people find great pleasure in the routine of housework. Fact: All people like to know their efforts are appreciated regardless of the work setting. Create a criticism jar and ask your family to put their gripes in the jar rather than on the table. P.S.: Be sure not to read them!

ON THE EDGE with Earl, Nadine & Weederman

BY JOE MARTIN & DR. JON CARLSON

I'M EXTREMELY NERVOUS AND CAN'T STOP BITING MY NAILS...

BUT ON THE PLUS SIDE I'M NOT HARD ON FURNITURE

www.catswithhands.com

"MY HUSBAND HAS A LOT OF GOOD HABITS SO I HATE TO MAKE AN ISSUE OF 'THE DRESSER DRAWERS LEFT OPEN', BUT IT IS DRIVING ME CRAZY!"

As Mark Twain said, "Nothing so needs reforming as other people's habits." Sometimes things just bother us. You need to do something without overreacting. Put the following note on each drawer, "When you leave me open, it makes (your name) go crazy!" It will make him smile as he develops another good habit.

"I CAN'T GET ANY SLEEP!"

As Honore de Balzac said, "A mother who is really a mother is never free." Fact: You can either **sleep** or you can **rest** - both are good for you. Parents of young children probably have to settle for **rest.** Arrange with your partner or another member of your support system for periodic nights to be "*off duty*".

"MY HUSBAND IS PROUD OF OUR SON BUT EVERY TIME HE TALKS ABOUT ONE OF HIS ACCOMPLISHMENTS, HE EXAGGERATES IT."

As Audrey Snead stated, "Some folks never exaggerate--they just remember big." Your husband is very proud of your son. Let him know how much you appreciate his being a supportive father. Accept the fact that the three "Es" of excitement, embellishment, and exaggeration are often part of the re-telling. Honesty may *not* always be the best policy when it comes to bragging about kids!!

"WHY DOES EVERYONE GIVE ME THE RUNAROUND? I'M EVEN DOING IT TO OTHERS!"

According to Groucho Marx, "There's one way to find out if a man is honest: ask him. If he says he is, you know he is crooked." Honesty is hard to give, as no one wants to hurt others. Stop giving others the *runaround* by providing honest answers. If others seem upset, let them know you are working at **taking the high road!!**

"I WONDER IF I MARRIED THE RIGHT ONE--I'M STARTING TO THINK ABOUT MY OLD BOYFRIENDS."

Fact: Many happily married people think about former partners. Good marriages have peaks and valleys. Develop strategies that lead you back to marriage. For starters, remember the first time you knew you loved your husband. As Karl Menninger said, "Love cures people-- both the ones who give it and the ones who receive it."

BY JOE MARTIN & DR. JON CARLSON

"I THINK MY HUSBAND AND I ACTUALLY ENJOY A GOOD ARGUMENT. IS THAT WRONG?"

Fact: Couples who argue and fight do not hate but are actually trying to get closer! Fighting can even lead to a pleasant physical response referred to as a "*wargasm*". It is not wrong to argue as long as there is no emotional or physical abuse. But don't forget the words of Muhammed Ali, "There are more pleasant things to do than beat up people."

"I'D LIKE MY WIFE TO HAVE A NICE WEDDING RING, BUT SHE WON'T PART WITH THE TINY OLD ONE."

People tend to give what they want and lose track of what the other person wants. As Dr. Richard Moss states, "The greatest gift you can give another is the purity of your attention." Listen to your wife and accept the fact that she cherishes her wedding ring. Ask her to make a list of some other ways that you can show her that you care.

Printed in the United States
56358LVS00003B/11-112

9 780974 596716